ChordTime Piano

Children's Songs

Sept. 19, 1998
Gloria has completed
all songs in this book.
Ms S. Pobe
(Teacher)

Level 2B

I-IV-V^7 chords in keys
of C, G and F

Arranged by

Nancy and Randall Faber

Production: Frank and Gail Hackinson
Production Coordinator: Marilyn Cole
Cover: Gwen Terpstra Design, San Francisco
Engraving: Music Craft of Hollywood, Inc. (Fla.)
Printer: Trend Graphics

THE
F·J·H
MUSIC
COMPANY
INC.

20432 Northeast 16th Place
North Miami Beach, Florida 33179

A NOTE TO TEACHERS

ChordTime Piano Children's Songs is a collection of popular songs that brings special enjoyment to children. The sense of fantasy and humor of the selections will motivate students to play while they learn basic harmony.

As the title **ChordTime** suggests, the emphasis of this book is on the student's mastery of I, IV and V^7 chords. The pieces are arranged in the keys of C, G and F with warm-up exercises for each key. Different accompanying styles have been chosen to expand the student's recognition and application of these chords.

ChordTime Piano Children's Songs is part of the *ChordTime Piano* series. "ChordTime" designates Level 2B of the PreTime to BigTime Piano Supplementary Library arranged by Faber and Faber. Following are the levels of the supplementary library which lead from *PreTime* to *BigTime*.

PreTime Piano	(Primer Level)
PlayTime Level	(Level 1)
ShowTime Piano	(Level 1B-2A)
Chordtime Piano	(Level 2B)
FunTime Piano	(Level 3)
BigTime Piano	(Level 4)

Each level offers books in a variety of styles, making it possible for the teacher to offer stimulating material for every student. For a complimentary detailed listing, write the publisher listed below.

Helpful Hints:

1. The chord warm-ups for a given key should be played daily before practicing the songs.

2. The student can be asked to identify the I, IV and V^7 chords in each song and write the correct chord symbol below the bass staff.

3. Hands-alone practice is recommended to facilitate correct fingering and accurate rhythm.

ISBN 0-929666-43-7

1☆

TABLE OF CONTENTS

Key of C

Practice these warm-ups before playing the songs in the key of C.

Warm-up 1

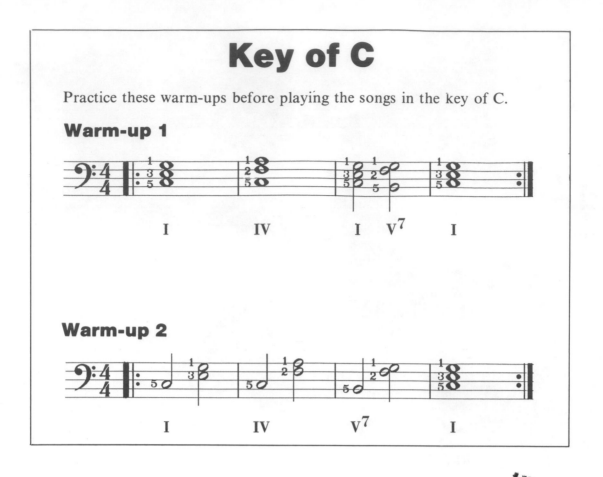

I   IV   I V⁷   I

Warm-up 2

I   IV   V⁷   I

In a Cabin in the Woods

English

Moderately fast

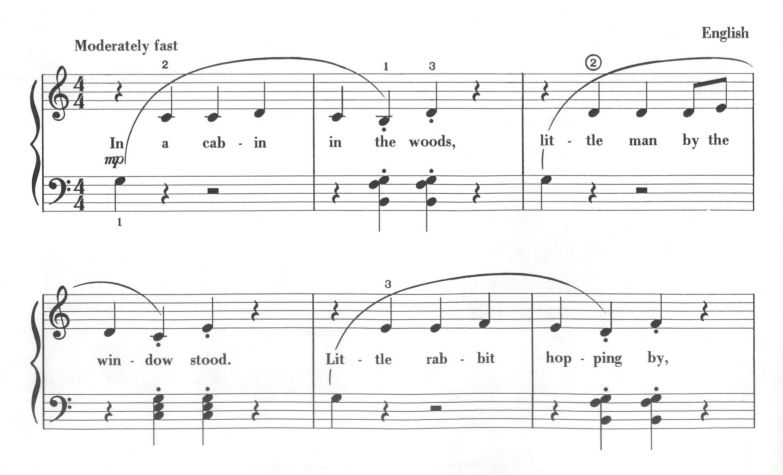

In a cab - in   in the woods,   lit - tle man by the

win - dow stood.   Lit - tle rab - bit   hop - ping by,

This arrangement © 1992 The FJH Music Company Inc.
International Copyright Secured.   Made in U.S.A.   All Rights Reserved.

FF 1041

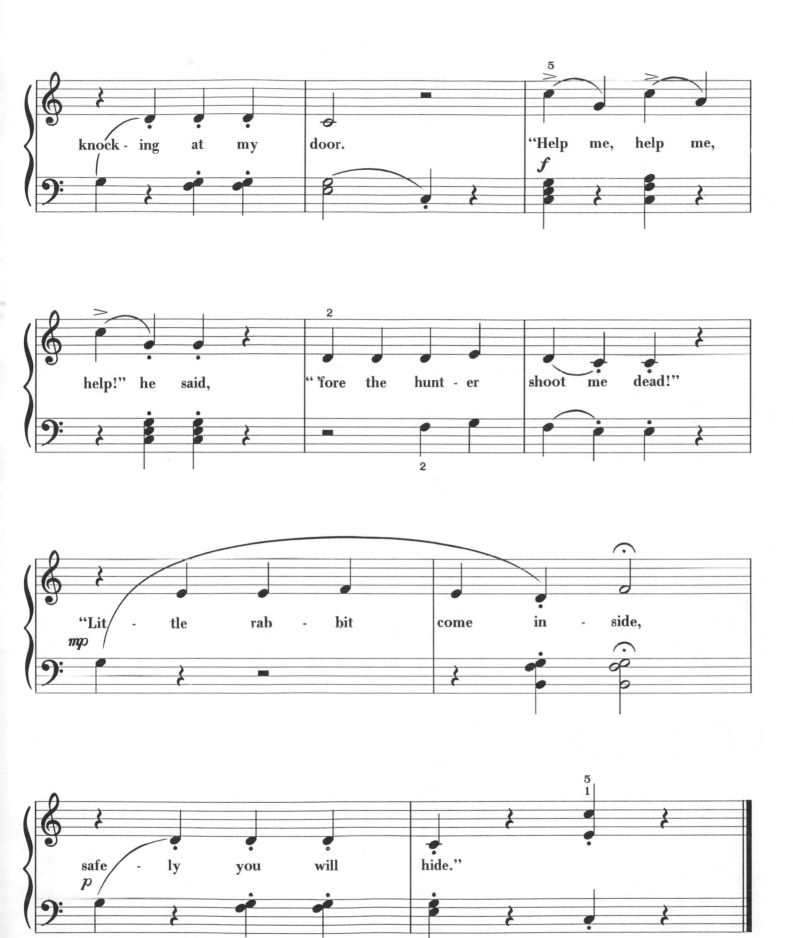

knock - ing at my door. "Help me, help me,

help!" he said, " 'fore the hunt - er shoot me dead!"

"Lit - tle rab - bit come in - side,

safe - ly you will hide."

Happy Birthday to You

Words and Music by
MILDRED J. HILL and PATTY S. HILL

FF 1041

Mama Paquita

Traditional Song from Brazil
English words by MARGARET MARKS

FF 1041

Catch a Falling Star

Words and Music by
PAUL J. VANCE and LEE POCKRISS

Ding-Dong! The Witch Is Dead
Featured in the M-G-M Picture "THE WIZARD OF OZ"

Lyric by E. Y. HARBURG

Music by HAROLD ARLEN

FF 1041

gone where the gob-lins go be - low, be - low, be - low, yo-

ho. Let's o - pen up and sing and ring the bells out.

Ding - dong! the mer-ry - o, sing it high, sing it low.

Let them know the wick - ed witch is dead.

Rubber Duckie

Words and Music by
JEFFREY MOSS

Key of G

Practice these warm-ups before playing the songs in the key of G.

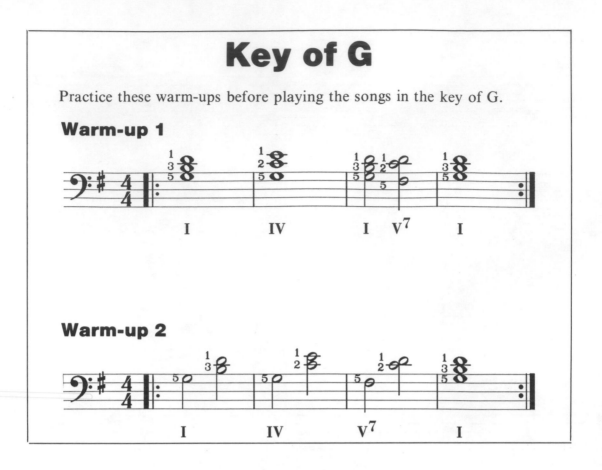

New River Train

Gospel

train, I'm rid - in' on that

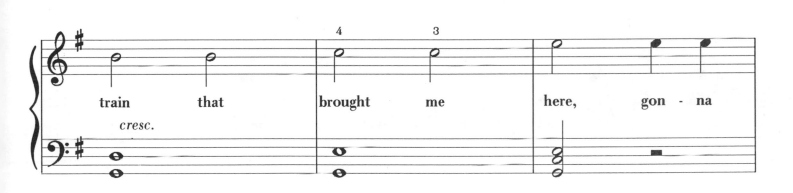

new riv - er train. _____ Same ole

train that brought me here, gon - na

cresc.

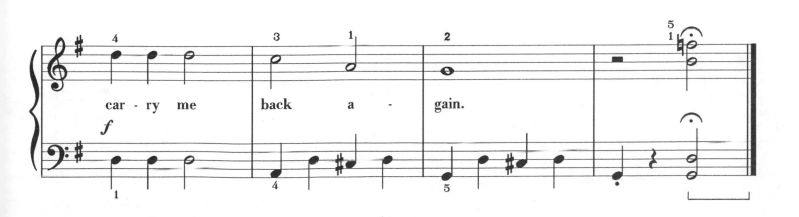

car - ry me back a - gain.

f

Pizza Time!

Lyric by CRYSTAL BOWMAN
Rather fast

Music by NANCY FABER

Six more piec - es, then I'll stop, wash it down with

so - da pop! Feel - ing just a lit - tle stuffed,

think that I have had e - nough. Pep - per - o - ni,

Slow and heavy

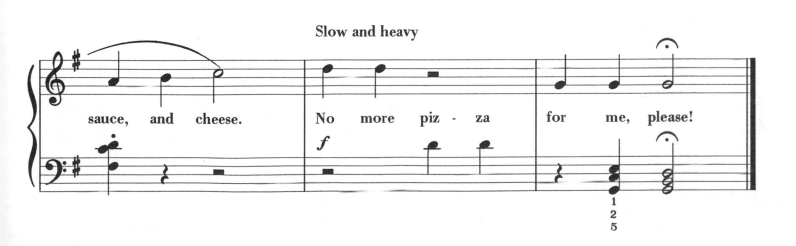

sauce, and cheese. No more piz - za for me, please!

Tingalayo

Jamaican Calypso Song

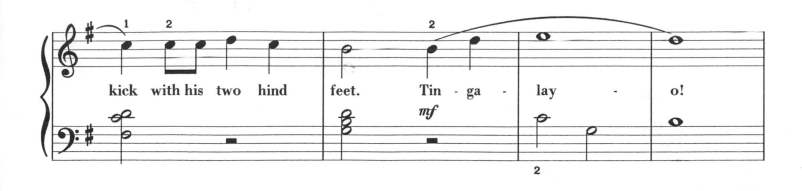

kick with his two hind feet. Tin - ga - lay - o!

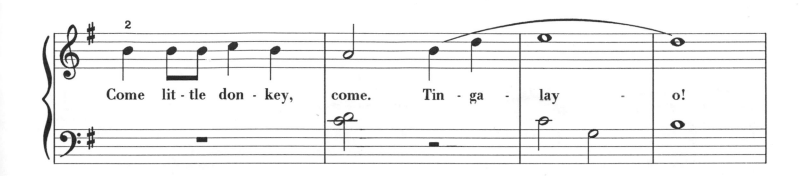

Come lit - tle don - key, come. Tin - ga - lay - o!

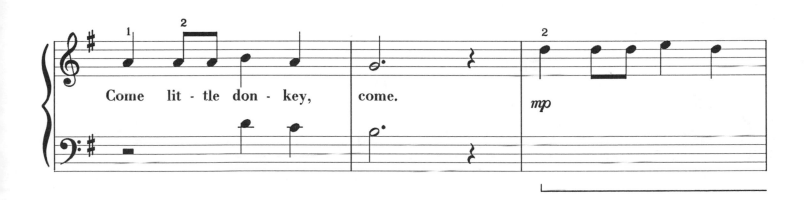

Come lit - tle don - key, come.

Happy Trails

Words and Music by
DALE EVANS

cares a - bout the clouds when we're to - geth - er? Just

sing a song and bring the sun - ny weath - er. Hap - py

trails to you, till we

meet a - gain.

Key of F

Practice these warm-ups before playing the songs in the key of F.

Warm-up 1

I   IV   I V⁷   I

Warm-up 2

I   IV   V⁷   I

I Can't Spell Hippopotamus

Words and Music by
J. FRED COOTS

Brightly, with a swing

I can spell "hat,"   H - A - T.   I can spell "cat,"   C - A - T.

I can spell "fat,"   F - A - T. But I   can't spell "hip- po -   pot- a-mus."

By permission of Toy Town Tunes Inc., c/o The Songwriters Guild of America.

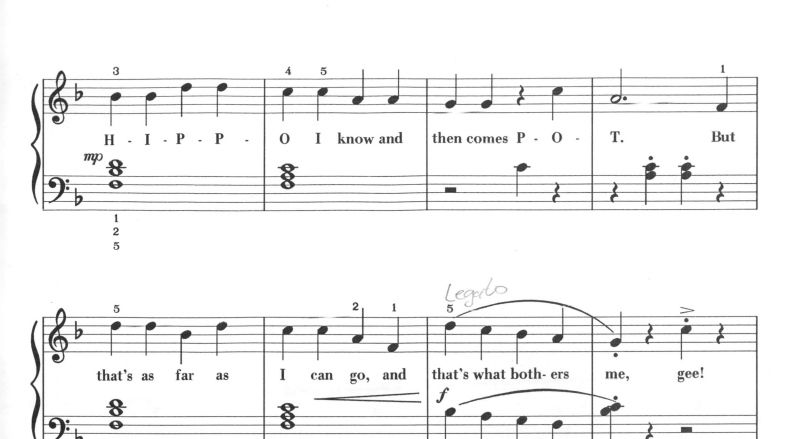

H - I - P - P - O I know and then comes P - O - T. But

that's as far as I can go, and that's what both- ers me, gee!

I can spell "dog," D - O - G. I can spell "log," L - O - G.

I can spell "hog," H - O - G. But I can't spell "hip - po - pot- a- mus."

Oh! Susanna

By Stephen Foster

Rhythm
♩. ♪

Lively

Oh, I come from Al - a - bam - a with my ban - jo on my

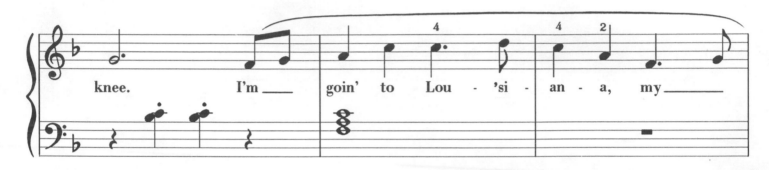

knee. I'm goin' to Lou - 'si - an - a, my

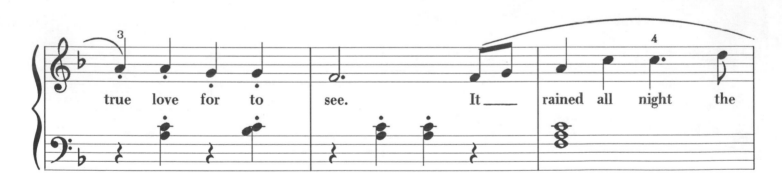

true love for to see. It rained all night the

day I left, the weath - er it was dry; The

sun so hot I froze to death, Su - san - na, don't you

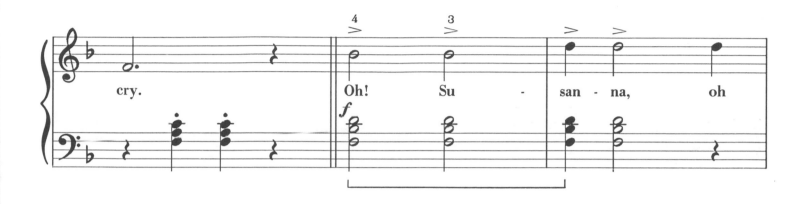

cry. Oh! Su - san - na, oh

don't you cry for me; For I come from Al - a -

bam - a with my ban - jo on my knee.

Teddy Bears' Picnic

Words by JIMMY KENNEDY

Music by JOHN W. BRATTON

Moderately fast (♩. = 88+)

If you go down in the woods to - day, you're
sure of a big sur - prise. If
you go down in the woods to - day, you'd
bet - ter go in dis - guise. For